To James, Sophie, and Henry   V.T.

Text copyright © 2009 Victoria Tebbs
Illustrations copyright © 2009 Russell Julian
This edition copyright © 2009 Lion Hudson

The moral rights of the author and illustrator
have been asserted

A Lion Children's Book
an imprint of
Lion Hudson plc
Wilkinson House, Jordan Hill Road,
Oxford OX2 8DR, England
www.lionhudson.com
UK ISBN 978 0 7459 6142 2
US ISBN 978 0 8254 7951 9

First edition 2009
This printing July 2009
1 3 5 7 9 10 8 6 4 2 0

A catalogue record for this book is available
from the British Library

Typeset in 22/27 Minion Pro
Printed and bound in Malaysia by Tien Wah Press (Pte) Ltd

Distributed by:
UK: Marston Book Services Ltd, PO Box 269, Abingdon, Oxon OX14 4YN
USA: Trafalgar Square Publishing, 814 N Franklin Street, Chicago, IL 60610
USA Christian Market: Kregel Publications, PO Box 2607, Grand Rapids, MI 49501

What Can You See?
On Christmas Night

Victoria Tebbs   *Illustrations by* Russell Julian

LI🐻N
CHILDREN'S

ople – Bethlehem! "Where shall we
y. Her baby was coming soon.
n doors but no one had room for them.

No room!

Long ago Mary and Joseph went on a jou

They walked and walked until… *what di*

At last they found a kind man.
"There's no room in my inn," said the man,
"but follow me outside."

munch

They walked in the moonlight until...
what did they see?

heehaw

A stable, warm and dry. So they
took shelter there, and in the
night Mary's baby was born.

moo

Mary wrapped him up snug and warm,
and laid him in the manger.

Out on the hillside that same night, shepherds were watching their sheep.

"What's that?" asked the shepherd boy.
Everyone looked and *what did they see?*

The sky was filled with a bright light.

Peace on earth!

baa

Goodwill to all!

"Good news!" said an angel. "God's Son has been born in Bethlehem. Go there and you will find him."

They left their sheep and hurried to Bethlehem.
Then, through one shining window,
what did they see?

cluck

Look!

Joseph watching, Mary smiling and in the manger little Baby Jesus… just as the angels had said.

Come in!

Look up there!

In a country far away lived wise men. One night, they had been watching the night sky, when *what did they see?*

A big bright star.
"It is the sign we have been waiting for," they cried. "A great king has been born! We must go and find him."

They journeyed for many miles following that star's light. At last, the star stopped by a stable. They went up to look and *what did they see?*

I bring myrrh

I bring frankincense

I bring gold

Baby Jesus, God's own Son.

heehaw

baa

And from that time, all around
the world, families have celebrated
Christmas to remember that special day
when Jesus was born.